Hi there!!! It's so nice to meet you! We are six fantastic fri

of an **amaaaaaaaazing** club called the 'Kind Kidz C

kind to ourselves, kind to other people and kind to

Because being kind is the best feeling ever and we think

Would you like to be in our club?

We have these super cool rucksacks which we like to fill with lots of tips and tools to help ourselves be the best we can be. Imagine you've got one too and lets go and see what we can find to put into our bag! Come on let's go!

First edition March 2021

Kind Kitty

Kitty was so kind that sometimes people even called her 'Kind Kitty'.

Let me tell you what Kitty did one lovely Summer's day. She was at the beach one beautiful afternoon with her Mum and Dad and little brother Jake. The sea was sparkling and the sun was shining so brightly and warm on their faces.

Kitty and her family were so hot that they decided to get an ice cream. I think it was the best ice cream they had ever had! A huge swirly, whirly ice cream with rainbow sprinkles and a chocolate filled cone too. Mmmmmm delicious!

Kitty and Jake felt so happy and could taste every amazing flavour in their mouths. But just then, WHOOSH! A seagull flew down and took Jake's ice cream right out of his hand. Oh no! He was so sad that the seagull had taken his yummy ice cream for his snack!

But do you know what happened next? Even though Kitty had only had one lick of her own ice cream, she did the kindest thing you could ever imagine. She gave her whole ice cream to Jake. She didn't like seeing him upset and just wanted to make him happy again. How kind is that? And even though she didn't have an ice cream anymore (although I'm sure Mum and Dad would have bought her another one) she felt so happy inside that she'd made someone else happy. She really was 'Kind Kitty'.

Now, the strangest thing happened after that. A little girl who had been watching Kitty decided that she wanted to do something kind too. So she looked around, spotted some rubbish on the floor and picked it up and put it in the bin.

How kind was that for looking after our planet?

The little girl's Mum was so proud of her that *she* wanted to do something kind too. She spotted an old man who was struggling to carry his deck chair and his fish and chips without dropping them all on the floor. So she ran over and helped the man to carry his things and set up his deck chair to eat his lunch.

How kind is that?

You see sometimes the kindest thing to do is think of someone else before yourself and create a giant ripple effect all over the world. Now wouldn't that be magical?

Put the gift of kindness into your bag and let's sing our song of Kindness all together........

I love to be kind

I love to be kind

It makes me feel happy inside my mind

Think about others not just I, me, my.

Healthy Hugo

Let's meet Hugo.

Hugo was a happy, helpful boy, who always had lots of fun. But one day, Hugo realised that there was something he wasn't very good at... being healthy. He didn't really do much exercise, he stayed up too late at night and he probably ate a few too many chips and sweets.
So sometimes, this made him feel a bit grumpy and tired. He decided that he was going to do an experiment. He decided that for one *whole* week he would be super healthy, to see how it made him feel.

So this is what he did. For breakfast, lunch and dinner, Hugo made really healthy choices, like lots of colourful fruits and vegetables and fresh food. He actually couldn't believe how delicious it all tasted.

Then instead of standing still in the playground at school each day, he ran around with all his friends, and skipped and jumped and flew around like a super hero. At home he kicked his ball around the garden and did silly dances in the kitchen.

Exercise was so much fun!

When it was time for bed, he didn't argue with his Mum and Dad, he just went straight upstairs because he knew that getting lots of sleep would help him to grow stronger and stronger. After he'd got his PJs on, he stood in front of the mirror and sang his special healthy song.

So what did Hugo realise? That he felt *amazing*! He had lots more energy and felt so good. He definitely realised that choosing to be healthy every day was a super smart, super hero choice.

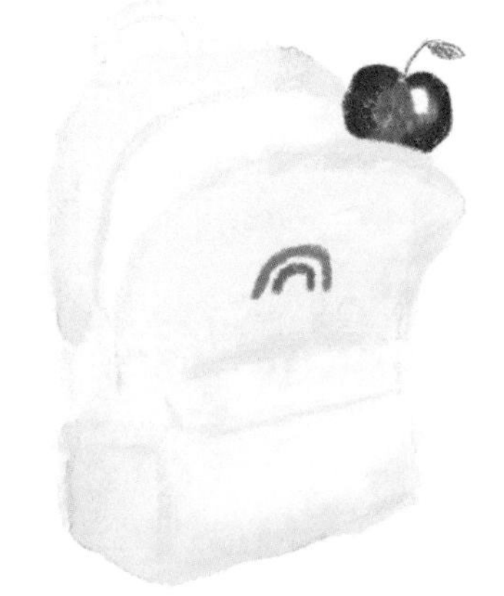

Pop the gift of health into your rucksack and let's sing our healthy song.

I am healthy, I am happy,

I'm the very best me

I will grow as tall as the
great oak tree

I am healthy, I am happy,

I'm the very best me

Come on let's be as healthy as can be.

Brave Bella

Bella was one of those girls who was always smiley and happy. But, she had a little bit of a secret, she wasn't very brave. Sometimes there were things she'd *really* like to do, but she just didn't feel brave enough to do them. She had some great ideas at school but she was too scared to put up her hand and share them.

She would love to try a class like Ballet, but was too nervous to see all those new faces.

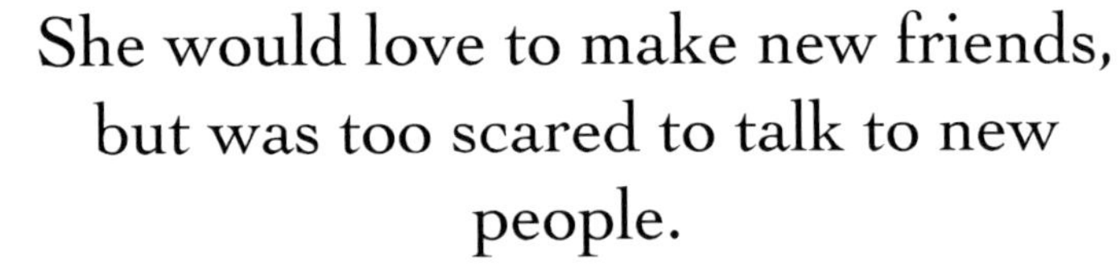

She would love to make new friends, but was too scared to talk to new people.

Bella thought that just maybe it was a bit of a shame to miss out on all these fun things because she was too scared. She *really* wanted to be braver and so she had an idea.

Whenever she wanted to do something but was a bit scared, she would close her eyes and imagine putting on a super shiny, bright and beautiful, BRAVE SUIT. How cool is that? This would make her feel *so* brave and give her the courage to know she could do anything she put her mind to.

So the next time the teacher asked someone in the class for the answer, she closed her eyes, imagined putting her brave suit on and........
put up her hand! She felt so great afterwards and knew she'd just become a tiny bit braver.

Then she started to use her brave suit everywhere! To try out that Ballet class she'd always wanted to, to make new friends and just be a sparkling, confident Bella. And the best thing was, she just kept getting braver and braver every time she wore the suit. We think you're amazing, Brave Bella!

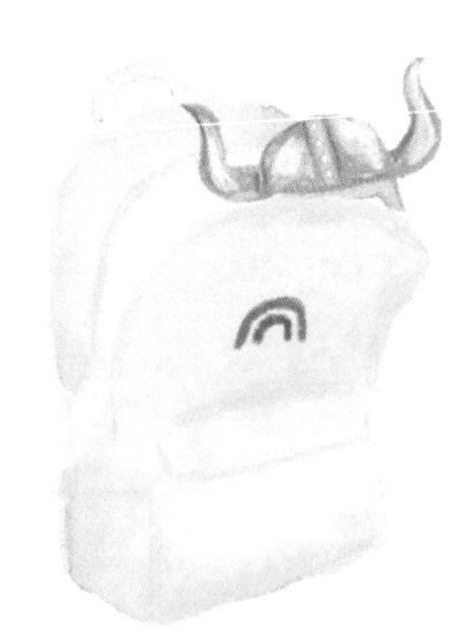

So, pop your brave gift into your bag and next time you need to, close your eyes and imagine putting YOUR brave suit on and know that you have all the courage you need inside of you.
Let's have a sing!

If I feel like i'm in a deep dark cave,

Time to stand tall and find my brave,

I can do it, I can do it, yes I can!

Time to stand tall and find my brave!

Brave, brave, brave said I!

Brave, brave, brave said I!

Brave, brave, brave said I!

If you can do it then so can I!

Calm Curtis

Let's meet Curtis.

With his curly hair and big brown eyes, he was caring and chatty and lots of fun.

Sometimes though, Curtis would get a bit angry when certain things happened. Such as when his little sister would ruin his lego tower, or his Mum said it was time to go home from the park, or even when he didn't want to get dressed in the morning. One time his Dad asked him to stop watching TV and Curtis got *so* angry. He jumped up and down and stamped and shouted and got himself all in a tizz!

Later on, when he had calmed down, he had a little think and realised he didn't really like the way he felt when he was angry. He felt hot and cross, and sometimes his head would hurt and his heart would beat really fast.

So, he decided to have a go at changing this, he looked into his rucksack to see what tool he might be able to use to help him. Aha! He found the perfect thing.

Later that day when his little sister grabbed his toy car and ran away with it, instead of getting really hot and angry like he usually did, he imagined getting a balloon out of his rucksack, and he took a HUGE breath in and blew all of his anger into the balloon. And he kept blowing it in until the balloon was really big and full of air.

And do you know what? Curtis felt much calmer and wasn't so mad anymore. He even asked his little sister nicely for the car back, and she gave it right to him.

He thought blowing up the balloon was a much better idea than shouting and screaming and he decided to always think of his balloon the next time he felt angry. Do you think you could do that too?

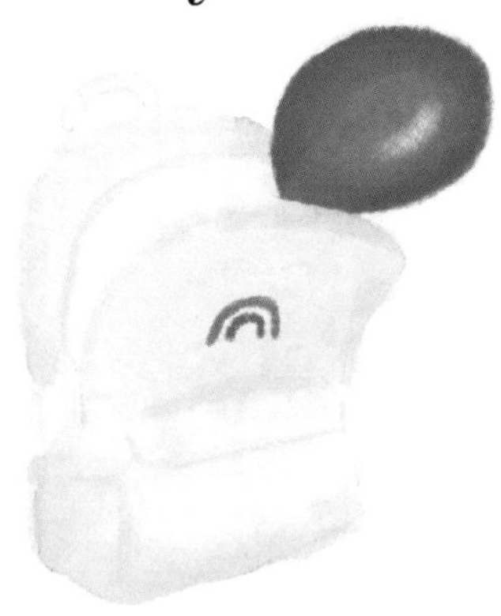

Pop the balloon inside your rucksack and then you'll know it's there next time you need it. Well done Calm Curtis! Let's sing our song!

I breathe in and I breathe out

I see my palm and I feel calm

I know I'm loved and that's enough.

Amazing Asher

So this is Asher, and he's pretty amazing! Do you know who else is amazing? YOU! Let's show you exactly why.

One day Asher was at the park and as he was looking around at all the other boys he thought "WOW! There are so many boys just like me. All as tall as me, same colour hair as me, they like playing football like me and they probably like the same games as me too."

But then he found out something *really* cool...

There was *no one* in the world exactly like him. He was the only one. And that made him feel super special. And that's the same with you. Only YOU have your exact finger prints, only YOU thinks your exact thoughts and only YOU can walk, talk, sing, jump and dance the way that YOU do it. You are made up of trillions of cells and no one in the world has the same ones as you. Isn't that incredible?

So you could go trekking around the world to find all 7 BILLION people on the planet and there would be nobody just like you. Wow!

Asher thought this was pretty cool and thought there was no point in ever trying to be like anyone else because each person in the world was so different in their own special way. This felt exciting and he couldn't wait to share his special gifts and talents with everyone he met.

Pop your "Amazing" gift in your bag and let's march to our song,

Amazing, amazing,

can't you see there's no one quite like me.

Amazing, amazing,

can't you see there's no one quite like me.

When you look in the mirror,

you should just say WOW!

Know that you are special,

turn and take a bow!

Grateful Gianna

Gianna was a bright and bubbly girl who loved to go on adventures and have lots of fun with her friends and family.

Once though, there was this very strange time when suddenly she couldn't do all of the things that she loved to do. It was like the world had gone to sleep for a little bit. The zoos and the farms all closed, the soft play centres were in darkness, the school gates were shut and the swimming pools were still.

What was even stranger was that she couldn't see her Grandma and Grandad, or play outside with all her friends. It was a funny old time.

There was a lot of playing at home, Mum pretending to be her school teacher, daily walks to the nearest park and video calls with Grandma!

As time went on, she began to feel a little lonely on her own.

She really missed seeing all the people who made her happy and going to all the places she loved.

After a while though, when things started to open again, Gianna couldn't believe how GRATEFUL she felt for every single thing that she had missed. She was grateful for a huge hug from Grandad, grateful to see her lovely school teacher, grateful to run around with her friends, grateful to jump into a pool, grateful to play in the playground, grateful to eat dinner in a restaurant and grateful to see the horses at the farm!

She just felt *so* grateful and it filled her heart and her body with so much love. She knew she would always enjoy these things just a little bit more from now on. You see, sometimes you don't realise how grateful you can be until things are gone. Now one of her favourite things to do is think of something she is grateful for right before she falls asleep every night. She can feel those lovely feelings of gratitude inside of her as she drifts off to sleep to dream away.

Let's put our feeling of gratitude into our bags and sing our song!

Grateful, grateful, grateful,
I'm feeling really grateful,
My hands, my nose, my feet, my toes.

Grateful, grateful, grateful,
I'm feeling really grateful,
The sky, the sun and feeling all the fun.

Grateful, grateful, grateful,
I'm feeling really grateful,
My family and happy me.

Grateful, grateful, grateful
I'm feeling really grateful.

I'm grateful! Really really grateful.
I'm grateful! Really really grateful.
I'm grateful! Really really grateful.

"To all the children of the world,

No act of kindness, however small, is ever wasted.

Spread kindness like sunshine and be the change.

The world needs you."

KIND KIDZ

Kindness starts with me

For more inspiration and resources come and find us at
www.kind-kidz.com
and Instagram
@kind.kidz